It's Easy To Play Bob Dylan.

Wise Publications
London/New York/Sydney

Exclusive Distributors:
Music Sales Limited
8/9 Frith Street, London W I V 5TZ, England.
Music Sales Corporation
225 Park Avenue South, New York, NY10003, USA.
Music Sales Pty Limited
I 20 Rothschild Avenue, Rosebery, NSW 2018, Australia.

This book © Copyright 1990 by
Special Rider Music
Order No. AM78890
UK ISBN 0.7 I 19.2178.4
US ISBN 0.8256.1277.2

Cover photograph by Kurt Gunther
Arranged by Frank Booth
Compiled by Peter Evans
Music processed by Musicprint
Typeset by Capital Setters

Music Sales' complete catalogue lists thousands of
titles and is free from your local music
shop, or direct from Music Sales Limited.
Please send £ I in stamps for postage to
Music Sales Limited, 8/9 Frith Street, London W I V 5TZ.

Printed in the United Kingdom by
Caligraving Limited, Thetford, Norfolk

All Along The Watchtower

Words & Music by Bob Dylan

Forever Young

Words & Music by Bob Dylan

stay for - ev - er young,

may you stay _____ for - ev - er young.

May you grow up to be right - eous, ___ may you

grow up to be true. May you al - ways know the

truth and see the lights sur - round - ing you. May you

al - ways be cou - ra - geous, stand up - right and be strong.

— May you stay for - ev - er

young, may you stay

for - ev - er young. May your

hands al - ways be bu - sy, may your feet al - ways be swift.

May you have a strong foun- da- tion when the

winds of chan- ges shift. May your heart al- ways __ be joy-

- ful, may your song al- ways be sung. __ May you

stay __ for- ev - er young, may you

stay __ for- ev - er young.

I'll Be Your Baby Tonight

Words & Music by Bob Dylan

2. Shut the light, shut the shade,
   You don't have to be afraid.
   I'll be your baby tonight.
   Well, that mocking bird's gonna
   Sail away, *etc.*

Baby, Stop Crying

Words & Music by Bob Dylan

CHORUS

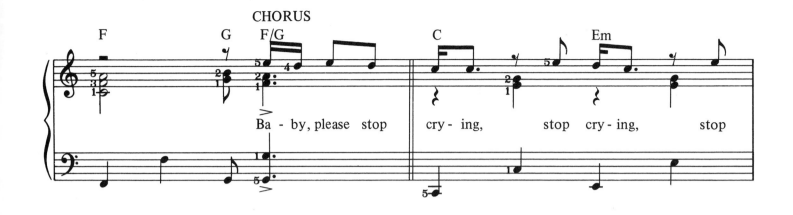

Ba - by, please stop cry - ing, stop cry - ing, stop

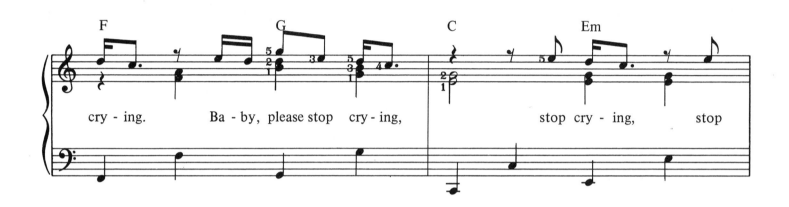

cry - ing. Ba - by, please stop cry - ing, stop cry - ing, stop

cry - ing. Ba - by, please stop cry - ing. You know, I know, the

sun will al - ways shine. So, ba - by, please stop cry - ing, 'cause it's

2. Go down to the river, babe.
   Honey, I will meet you there.
   Go down to the river, babe.
   Honey, I will pay your fare.
      (To Chorus)

3. If you're looking for assistance, babe,
   Or if you just want some company,
   Or if you just want a friend you can talk to,
   Honey, come and see about me.
      (To Chorus)

4. You been hurt so many times,
   And I know what you're thinking of.
   Well, I don't have to be no doctor, babe,
   To see that you're madly in love.
      (To Chorus)

If You See Her, Say Hello

Words & Music by Bob Dylan

Moderately slow

mp If you see ___ her, say hel - lo, ___ she

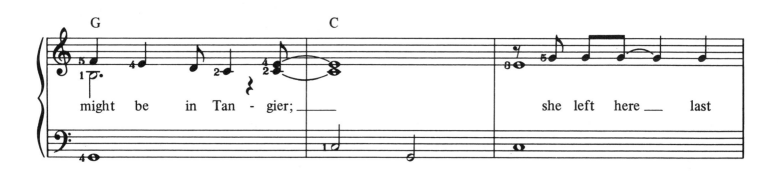

might be in Tan - gier; ___ she left here ___ last

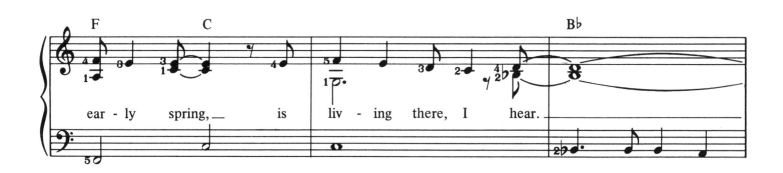

ear - ly spring, ___ is liv - ing there, I hear. ___

___ Say for me ___ that I'm al - right, ___ though

things get kind of slow; _____ she might think that I've for -

got-ten her, don't tell her it is-n't so.

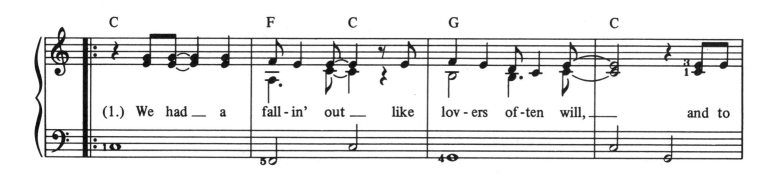

(1.) We had __ a fall-in' out __ like lov - ers of-ten will, __ and to

think of how __ she left that night __ it still brings me a chill.

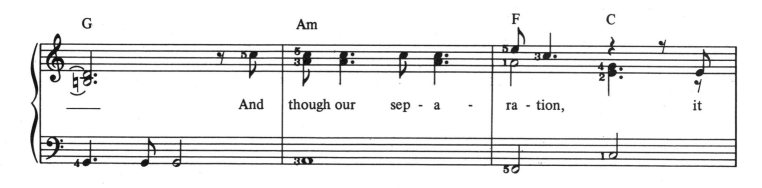

And though our sep - a - ra - tion, it

pierced me to the heart, ____ she still lives ____ in-

side of me, we've nev - er been a - part.

If you ____ get close to her, ____

kiss her once for me; ____ I al - ways have re -

spect- ed her ____ for bust - ing out and get - tin' free. ____

2. I see a lot of people as I make the rounds,
And I hear her name here and there as I go from town to town.
And I've never gotten used to it, I've just learned to turn it off;
Either I'm too sensitive or else I'm getting soft.
Sundown, yellow moon, I replay the past;
I know ev'ry scene by heart — they all went by so fast.
If she's passin' back this way I'm not that hard to find;
Tell her she can look me up if she's got the time.

Knockin' On Heaven's Door

Words & Music by Bob Dylan

CHORUS

2. Mama, put my guns in the ground,
   I can't shoot them anymore;
   That long black cloud is comin' down,
   I feel like I'm knockin' on heaven's door.
   (To Chorus)

If Not For You

Words & Music by Bob Dylan

If not for you,—

Babe, I'd lay a - wake all night,—

wait for the mor - nin' light — to shine in

through,— but it would not be

new — if not for you.

If not for you my sky would fall; rain would gath - er too. _____ with - out your love I'd be no - where at all; I'd be lost if not for you and you know it's true.

couldn't hear the robin sing;

I just wouldn't have a clue.

Anyway, it wouldn't ring true,

if not for you.

If not for you.

28

Lay, Lady, Lay

Words & Music by Bob Dylan

I'll show them to you

and you'll see them shine

Lay, la-dy, lay,___ lay a-cross my big brass bed.___

Stay, la-dy, stay,___ stay with your man___ a-while.___

Un-til the break of___ day,___

let me see you make him smile.___

One Of Us Must Know
(Sooner Or Later)

Words & Music by Bob Dylan

you just hap - pened to be there, that's all. ____

When I saw you say "good - bye" ____

to your friend and smile

I thought that it was well ____

____ un - der - stood ____

that you'd be com - in' back

in a lit - tle while;

I did - n't know ____ that you were

2. I couldn't see what you could show me;
Your scarf had kept your mouth well hid.
I couldn't see how you could know me,
But you said you knew me, and I believed you did.
When you whispered in my ear and asked me
If I was leavin' with you or her
I didn't realize just what I did hear
I didn't realize how young you were.
(To Chorus)

3. I couldn't see when it started snowin',
Your voice was all that I heard.
I couldn't see where we were goin'
But you said you knew, an' I took your word.
And then you told me later, as I apologized
That you were just kiddin' me, you weren't really from the farm,
An' I told you, as you clawed out my eyes
That I never really meant to do you any harm.
(To Chorus)

Pledging My Time

Words & Music by Bob Dylan

3. Won't you come with me, baby?
   I'll take you where you wanna go.
   And if it don't work out,
   You'll be the first to know.
   I'm pledging my time to you,
   Hopin' you'll come through, too.

4. *(Instrumental)*

5. Well, the room is so stuffy,
   I can hardly breathe.
   Ev'rybody's gone but me and you,
   And I can't be the last to leave.
   I'm pledging my time . . . *etc.*

6. Well, they sent for the ambulance
   And one was sent.
   Somebody got lucky,
   But it was an accident.
   Now I'm pledging my time . . .*etc.*

Quinn, The Eskimo

Words & Music by Bob Dylan

2. Now, I likes to do just like the rest,
   I likes my sugar sweet,
   But guarding fumes and making haste
   You know it ain't my cup of meat.
   Ev'rybody's out there feeding pigeons
   Out on a limb,
   But when Quinn, the Eskimo gets here,
   The pigeons' gonna run to him.
   (To Chorus)

3. A cow's moo and a cat's meow,
   You know I can't recite them all;
   Tell me where it hurts you, honey,
   And I'll tell you who to call.
   Nobody can get any sleep,
   You know there's someone on ev'rybody's toes
   But when the Eskimo gets here,
   Ev'rybody's gonna want to doze.
   (To Chorus)

This Wheel's On Fire

Words by Bob Dylan
Music by Rick Danko

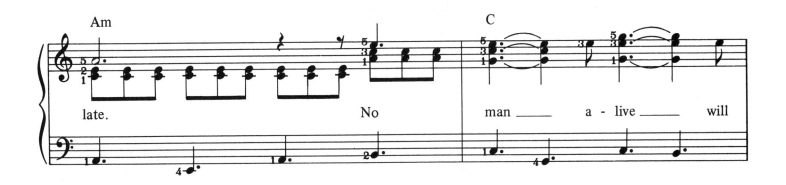

late. No man ____ a - live ____ will

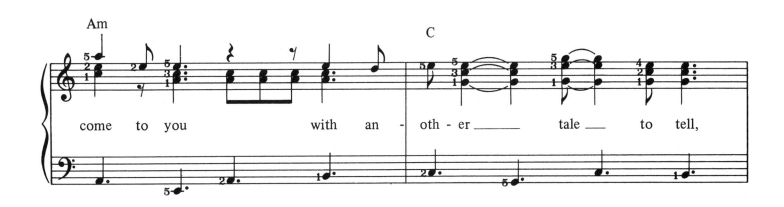

come to you with an - oth - er ____ tale ____ to tell,

But you know ____ that we ____ shall

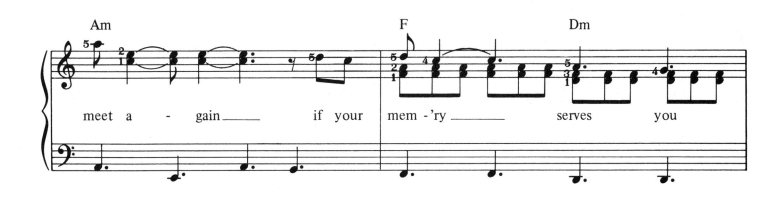

meet a - gain ____ if your mem -'ry ____ serves you

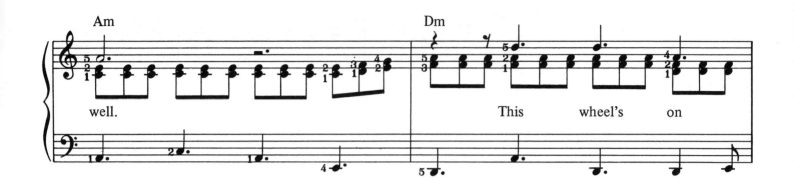

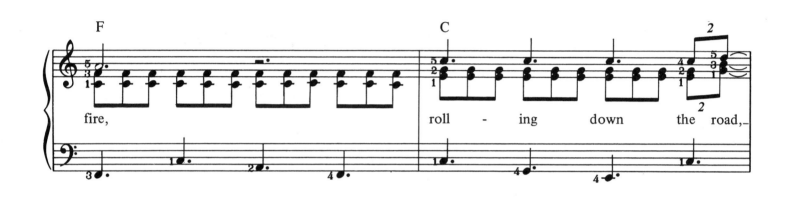

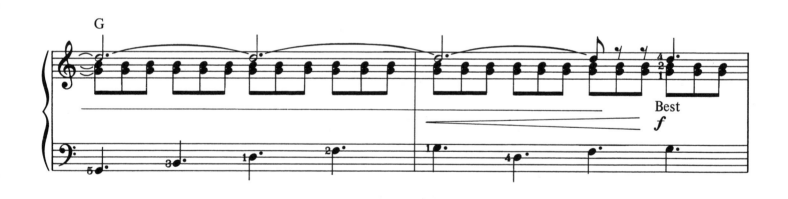

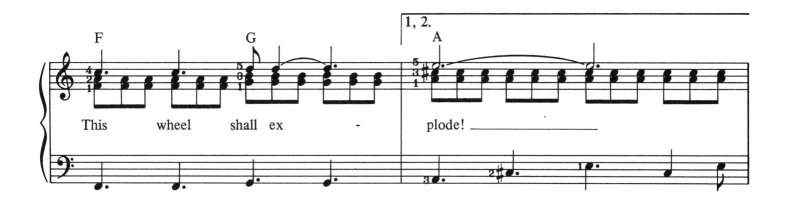

This wheel shall ex - plode! _____

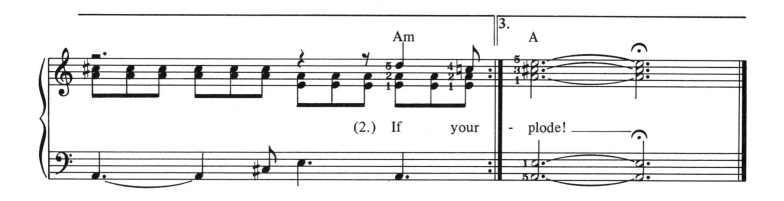

(2.) If your - plode! _____

2. If your mem'ry serves you well,
   I was goin' to confiscate your lace,
   And wrap it up in a sailors knot
   And hide it in your case.
   If I knew for sure that it was yours
   But it was oh so hard to tell.
   But you knew that we would meet again,
   If your mem'ry serves you well.
   This wheel's on fire . . . . etc.

3. If your mem'ry serves you well,
   You'll remember you're the one that called on me
   To call on them to get you your favours done.
   And after ev'ry plan had failed
   And there was nothing more to tell,
   You knew that we would meet again,
   If your mem'ry served you well.
   This wheel's on fire . . . . etc.

You Ain't Goin' Nowhere

Words & Music by Bob Dylan

2. I don't care how many letters they sent,
   Morning came and morning went.
   Pick up your money and pack your tent,
   You ain't goin' nowhere.
   (To Chorus)

3. Buy me a flute and a gun that shoots,
   Tail-gates and substitutes.
   Strap yourself to the tree with roots,
   You ain't goin' nowhere.
   (To Chorus)